U0063420

用英文說故事

多的是你不知道的事

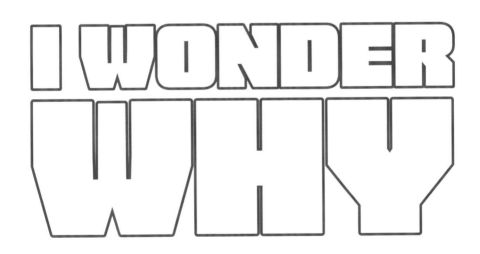

Aa

above 在……上面 prep. [əˋbʌv]

A bird can fly high above our heads because they have strong muscles that help them flap their wings.

因為鳥有強壯的肌肉幫助牠們拍打翅膀，所以牠們可以在人類的頭上飛。

afraid 害怕的；擔憂的 adj. [əˋfred]

When a skunk feels afraid, it lets out a stinky smell that is worse than the smell of a fart.

當臭鼬感到害怕時，牠散發出的臭味比放屁的味道還臭。

airplane 飛機 n. [ˋɛrˌplen]

Airplanes are shaped like birds to help them fly. The shape keeps the wind from slowing the airplane down and the wings are like a bird's wings.

飛機的形狀像鳥以幫助飛行，這種形狀可防止風使飛機減速，而機翼就如同鳥的翅膀一般。

animal 動物 n. [ˋænəmɪ]

Animals are very cute, but we also need them to keep earth healthy. Every animal has a job to help the environment.

動物很可愛，然而我們也需要牠們來維護地球的健康。每種動物都有著保護環境的職責。

answer 答案；回答 n. [ˋænsɚ]

If you don't know the answer to a question, you can always ask your mom or dad.

如果你不知道問題的答案，你隨時可以詢問你的父母。

acorn 橡實；橡子 n. [ˋekɔrn]

Squirrels bury acorns in the ground to save them for the winter.

松鼠將橡實埋藏在地底下以保存它們過冬。

apple 蘋果 n. [ˋæpḷ]

An apple seed can be planted to grow an apple tree, which will grow more apples.

一顆蘋果籽可以種植成蘋果樹，蘋果樹會長出更多的蘋果。

ask 詢問；請求 v. [æsk]

You will learn more about the world if you ask many questions.

如果踴躍地發問，你會更了解這個世界。

asleep 睡著的 adj. [ə`slip]

The brown bat is asleep for 20 hours of the day. He is only awake for about 4 hours a day!

棕蝠一天睡20個小時，
只有大約4個小時是醒著！

awake 醒著的 adj. [ə`wek]

A giraffe is awake almost all day, every day! It only sleeps 30 minutes or less each day!

長頸鹿幾乎整天都醒著的！
每天只睡三十分鐘，甚至更少！

awesome 令人敬畏的、驚嘆的 adj. [`ɔsəm]

Learning about science and nature can be an awesome adventurer!

學習自然與科學可以成為令人敬畏的冒險家！

Bb

balance 平衡 v. [ˋbæləns]

When you try to balance on one leg, if there is more weight on one side, gravity will pull the heavier side down.

當你試著用一隻腳平衡時，如果一邊重量較大，重力會把較重的一邊往下拉。

ball 球；球狀物 n. [bɔl]

A ball will stop rolling on flat ground because of something called friction. Friction is the force between the ball and the ground that makes the ball slow down.

球會因為摩擦力而停止在平地上滾動。
摩擦力是球和地面接觸時使球變慢的阻力。

bicycle 腳踏車 n. [ˋbaɪsɪkḷ]

When you push the pedal on a bicycle, the wheels turn around and round.

當你踩腳踏車的踏板時，車輪會不停轉動。

big 大的（尺寸或數量） adj. [bɪg]

A blue whale is twenty-five times bigger than an elephant! In fact, the blue whale's tongue is about the same size as one elephant!

藍鯨比大象大二十五倍！
事實上，藍鯨的舌頭和
一隻大象差不多大！

bird 鳥；禽 n. [bɝd]

The smallest bird is called a bee hummingbird. It's only a little bit bigger than a bee.

最小的鳥叫蜜蜂蜂鳥，
牠只比蜜蜂大一點。

block 一塊；積木 n. [blɑk]

Try stacking your toy blocks.
Count how many you can stack
as you go!

試著把你的積木一塊一塊堆起
來。數一數你能堆多少！

body 身體；軀幹 n. [`bɑdɪ]

The main parts of the body are
the head, neck, torso, arms, and legs.

身體的主要部位是頭部、
頸部、軀幹、手臂和腳。

book 書 n. [bʊk]

The more books you read, the smarter
you will get.

你讀的書越多就越聰明。

bored 感到無聊、厭煩的 adj. [bɔrd]

Whenever you feel bored, ask your mom and dad if you can go explore the world outside. There is so much to learn.

每當你感到無聊時，問問你的父母，你是否可以去探索外面的世界。還有很多值得學習的事。

bounce 彈起；反彈 v. [bauns]

How high can you bounce your ball? The more force and energy you put into throwing your ball, the higher it will bounce!

你的球可以彈多高呢？丟球時你投入的力量越多，球就會彈得越高！

box 箱；盒 n. [bɑks]

House cats love to play in boxes. Many cats will treat a box like their home. It feels like a safe place for them to hide. So, if you have a cardboard box at home, give it to a cat.

家貓喜愛在箱子裡玩。許多貓會將箱子當成是牠們的家。感覺是一個安全可以躲藏的地方。所以，如果你家有紙箱的話，把它給貓吧。

bubble 泡泡；氣泡 n. [ˋbʌbḷ]

You can make your own bubbles by mixing dish soap with a little bit of water and sugar. Then, cover a bubble wand with your mixture and blow out some bubbles!

你可以用洗碗精加一點點水和糖自己做泡泡。然後把混合物蓋上泡沫棒，就能吹出一些泡泡！

bus 公車；大客車 n. [bʌs]

How many buses can you count? Look outside and count all of the buses that drive by.

往外看，數一數所有行駛中的公車，你能數出有多少輛公車嗎？

butterfly 蝴蝶 n. [ˋbʌtɚˌflaɪ]

Have you ever seen a caterpillar become a beautiful butterfly?

你有看過毛毛蟲變成美麗的蝴蝶嗎？

TRY IT

1. You can see birds and airplanes flying high _____ us in the sky.
   你可以看到鳥和飛機飛在我們之上的天空。

2. An _____ is a tasty fruit that grows on trees.
   蘋果是生長在樹上的美味水果。

3. Sloths and turtles are two of the slowest _____ in the world.
   樹懶和烏龜是世界上行動最慢的兩種動物。

4. A caterpillar wraps itself up in a cocoon and, after a few days, comes out as a _____ with beautiful wings.
   毛毛蟲將自己包裹在繭中，幾天後，變成一隻有著美麗翅膀的蝴蝶。

5. I tried to _____ a cup of water on my head, but it fell over, and I was covered in water!
   我試著平衡頭上的一杯水，但水翻倒了，我被水淋濕。

6. How high can you stack your toy _____?
   你可以把積木堆成多高？

Answer

1. above
2. apple
3. animals
4. butterfly
5. balance
6. blocks

Cc

cage 籠子 n. [kedʒ]

A cage can help keeps animals safe. But, do you think this is a nice place to keep animals? If you were an animal, would you rather be in a cage or out in the wild?

籠子有助於保護動物的安全。但你認為這是飼養動物的好地方嗎？如果你是動物，你寧願被關在籠子裡還是在野外？

car 汽車 n. [kɑr]

If we could drive a car to the moon, it would take about six months to get there!

如果我們能開車去月球，大約需要六個月的時間才能到那裡！

12

claw 腳爪 n. [klɔ]

A sloth uses its very long claws to hang from trees and as a weapon when it's in danger.

樹懶用牠很長的爪子掛在樹上，當遇到危險時則作為武器。

climb 攀爬；上升 v. [klaɪm]

Cats can climb up trees, but they have a hard time coming down. This is because their back legs are stronger than their front. They can use their back legs to push up, but when they come down, their front legs aren't strong enough to hold them up.

貓可以爬樹但卻很難下來。這是因為貓的後腿比前腿強壯，牠們可以用後腿向上推，但當下來時，前腿沒有足夠的力量來支撐牠們。

cloud 雲 n. [klaʊd]

Fluffy white clouds means there will not be any rain soon, but gray clouds means it is going to rain. Dark clouds means that is has already rained. Look up. What color are the clouds right now?

蓬鬆的白雲意味著短時間內不會下雨，但灰色的雲代表快要下雨。烏雲則是已經下雨了。抬頭看看，現在的雲是什麼顏色呢？

color 顏色 n. [ˋkʌlɚ]

If you mix all the colors of the rainbow together, you will get black.

如果你把彩虹的所有顏色混合在一起，就會變成黑色。

confused 困惑的；糊塗的 adj. [kənˋfjuzd]

Whenever I am confused about something, I know that I can ask my teacher to explain it to me.

當我對某件事感到困惑時，我知道我可以請教老師來解釋給我聽。

cozy 舒適的；溫馨的 adj. [`kozɪ]

When the seasons start to change, some animals, like hedgehogs and bears, find a cozy spot and sleep for most of the winter. This is called hibernation.

當季節開始變換時，有些動物像是刺蝟和熊，會找個舒適的地方，並在冬天大部分的時間睡覺。這叫作冬眠。

crab 螃蟹 n. [kræb]

Crabs not only walk sideways, they swim sideways too!

螃蟹不僅是側身走路，牠們也是側身游泳！

crayon 蠟筆 n. [`kreən]

Do you think all colors of crayons melt at the same speed? Try this experiment at home with your mom or dad. Melt different colored crayons with a hairdryer. Which crayon melted the fastest?

你認為所有蠟筆的顏色都以相同的速度融化嗎？在家裡和父母試試這個實驗，用吹風機融化不同顏色的蠟筆，哪一隻蠟筆會融化得最快？

creature 生物；動物 n. [ˋkritʃɚ]

When you go camping, you will be able to hear the sounds of birds and other creatures at night. The animals making those noises are called nocturnal animals because they sleep in the day and are awake at night.

當你去露營時，能夠在夜間聽到鳥類和其他生物的聲音。發出這些聲音的動物稱為夜行性動物，因為牠們在白天睡覺，晚上是醒著。

crow 烏鴉 n. [kro]

Scarecrows are made to look like humans to scare birds, like crows, away from their fields.

稻草人做成像人類的樣子來嚇烏鴉等鳥類，讓牠們遠離田地。

curious 好奇的 adj. [ˋkjʊrɪəs]

It's good to be curious about the world. The more curious you are, the more you will want to learn. The more you want to learn, the smarter you get!

對世界充滿好奇是件好事，你越好奇，就會越想要學習。你想學得越多，你就會變得越聰明！

16

Dd

daisy 雛菊 n. [ˋdezɪ]

A daisy is a flower with a yellow center and white petals. You can find daisies in every part of the world except in Antarctica.

雛菊是一種有著黃色花蕊和白色花瓣的花。除了南極洲，你可以在世界各地看到雛菊。

deep 深的；向下延伸的 adj. [dip]

The deepest part of the ocean that we know about is called the Mariana Trench. It is near the Philippines.

我們所知道最深的海溝叫做馬里亞納海溝。它位於菲律賓附近。

17

different 不同的；有差別的 adj. [`dɪfərənt]

Everyone is different. It is important to learn about each other's differences so that we can learn more and get along with each other.

每個人都是不同的。瞭解彼此的差異很重要，這樣我們不僅能學習到更多並且與彼此相處。

dig 挖；挖掘 v. [dɪg]

Archeologists dig into the ground at places all over the world to find old bones of dinosaurs.

考古學家在世界各地挖掘，尋找恐龍的遺骸。

dinosaur 恐龍 n. [ˈdaɪnəˌsɔr]

Can you imagine what it would be like to stand next to a huge dinosaur? It's too bad we can't do this these days. All the dinosaurs went extinct 65,000,000 years ago. That's a long time ago!

你能想像站在一隻巨大的恐龍旁邊會是什麼樣子嗎？可惜現在我們無法體會，所有的恐龍在六千五百萬年前就滅絕了。那是很久以前的事了！

dirt 泥土；灰塵 n. [dɝt]

Some scientists study dirt to learn more about the earth and weather. Many living things live in dirt.

有些科學家利用研究泥土來更瞭解地球和氣候。也有許多生物生活在泥土中。

dirty 髒的 adj. [`dɝtɪ]

Science is fun, but you can get pretty dirty doing experiments. Always be sure to wear clothes that you don't mind getting dirty when you are doing experiments.

科學很有趣，但做實驗時你會弄髒。做實驗時要確保穿著你不介意被弄髒的衣服。

dizzy 眩暈的；眼花撩亂的 adj. [`dɪzɪ]

When you spin your body round and around then stop, you get dizzy because the fluid keeps spinning in your ears.

當你一直旋轉身體然後停下來，你會頭暈是因為液體不斷地在你耳朵裡旋轉。

do 做 v. [du]

You can do it!
你可以做到！

dog 狗 n. [dɔg]

Why do dogs smell each other's butts? A dog can learn about the other dog's age, and how healthy it is by sniffing the other dog's butt.

為什麼狗會互相聞屁股？狗可以藉由聞屁股知道彼此的年齡和健康狀況。

doll 玩偶 n. [dɑl]

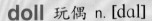

Have you ever made your own doll? Instead of buying one, try making one with some scrap fabric, glue, and old socks. Ask your parents for help.

你曾經做過自己的玩偶嗎？與其買一個，不如請你的父母幫忙，試著用一些廢布、膠水和舊襪子做一個。

down 在下面；向（朝）下 adv. [daun]

On earth, if you drop something,
it falls down to the ground.

在地球上，如果將東西往下丟，
會落在地上。

drop 掉落 v. [drap]

In outer space, if you drop
something, it floats.

如果你在外太空掉了東西，
它會浮起來。

TRY IT

1. I think it is going to rain. That _____ is grey.
   我想快要下雨了，那朵雲是灰色的。

2. To help prevent pollution, it is better to walk or ride a bike instead of driving a _____.
   為了防止汙染，最好是走路或騎腳踏車，而不是開車。

3. Tigers use their long _____ to kill smaller animals.
   老虎用長爪子殺死較小動物。

4. If I _____ my keys down a hole, what are some ways that I can get them back?
   如果我的鑰匙掉進洞裡，有什麼方法可以拿回來？

5. Spinning around and around makes me feel so _____.
   一圈又一圈地旋轉讓我感到頭暈。

6. My dog likes to _____ holes in the ground to bury his bones.
   我的狗喜歡在地上挖洞埋牠的骨頭。

Answer

1. cloud	2. car	3. claws
4. drop	5. dizzy	6. dig

Ee

ear 耳朵 n. [ɪr]

Do you think rabbits can hear better than people since their ears are so big? They sure can. Loud noises can really bother them!

你認為兔子的聽力比人好是因為牠們的耳朵很大？的確是。吵雜的噪音真的會困擾牠們！

early 提早的；早期的 adj. [`ɝlɪ]

Why do roosters crow so early in the morning? Roosters crow to tell other roosters they are awake and ready to fight!

為什麼公雞在清晨這麼早啼叫？雞鳴聲是在告訴其他公雞，牠們醒了準備戰鬥！

earth 地球 n. [ɜθ]

Earth, our home, is the third planet from the sun and the only planet with oxygen.

地球，我們的家，是太陽系的第三顆行星，也是唯一一顆有氧氣的星球。

east 東方；東 n. [ist]

The sun rises in the east because the earth spins towards the east.

太陽從東方升起是因為地球向東旋轉。

eat 吃 v. [it]

It's important that you eat a lot of vegetables every day to get enough vitamins for your body to grow.

每天吃大量的蔬菜以獲得足夠的維生素，對你身體的成長是很重要的。

egg 雞蛋 n. [ɛg]

What do you think came first: the chicken or the egg? You need a chicken to lay an egg, but you also need an egg to hatch a chicken.

你覺得是先有雞？還是先有蛋？你需要一隻雞來產卵，但也需要一個雞蛋孵化成一隻雞。

elder 長輩；長者 n. [`ɛldɚ]

Your elders have lived a very long time and are very smart. Ask them questions when you want to know the answer to something.

你的長輩們活了很長的時間也很聰明。當你想知道某些事的答案就問他們問題。

elephant 大象 n. [`ɛləfənt]

Elephants are the world's largest land animal.

大象是世界上最大的陸地動物。

emotion 情緒；感情 n. [ɪˋmoʃən]

Do you think animals can feel emotions like happiness, sadness, and loneliness? They sure can! Scientists have proved it. So, it is very important that we are nice to animals because they can feel sad just like you!

你認為動物能感受到情緒，像是快樂、悲傷或是孤獨嗎？牠們的確可以！科學家曾經證實過。所以友善的對待動物很重要，因為動物跟你一樣會感受到悲傷！

enjoy 享受；喜愛 v. [ɪnˋdʒɔɪ]

Do you enjoy reading books?

你喜歡看書嗎？

entire 全部的；完整的 [ɪnˋtaɪr]

There are about 1,000,000,000,000,000,000,000 stars in the entire universe!

整個宇宙中約有 1,000,000,000,000,000,000,000 顆恆星！

evening 傍晚；晚上 n. [ˋivnɪŋ]

Nocturnal animals, like owls, come out in the evening and stay up all night.

夜行性動物像是貓頭鷹，牠都是在晚上出現，徹夜不睡。

exercise 運動；鍛鍊 v. [ˋɛksɚˏsaɪz]

It is important to exercise because it keeps your body healthy.

運動很重要，因為能保持你的身體健康。

experiment 實驗 n. [ɪkˋspɛrəmənt]

An experiment is a way to test something. What color does red and blue make? You can find out by mixing blue and red paint. That's an experiment.

實驗是測試某種東西的一種方式。什麼顏色是由紅色和藍色組成？你可以將藍色和紅色的油漆混合後得知。這就是實驗。

extinct 滅絕的；絕種的 adj. [ɪk`stɪŋkt]

Dinosaurs went extinct 65 million years ago when a giant comet crashed into earth.

六千五百萬年一顆巨大的彗星墜入地球使得恐龍滅絕。

eye 眼睛 n. [aɪ]

How does an eagle find food from so high up in the sky? An eagle's eye is so strong that it can see eight times better than a person can.

一隻老鷹是如何從高空覓食的？老鷹的眼睛很厲害，視力比人類好八倍。

face 臉 n. [fes]

A person's face has more muscles than anywhere else in the body. These muscles help us show our emotions.

人的臉比身體任何部位都有更多的肌肉。這些肌肉能夠幫助我們表現出情緒。

fall 跌倒 v. [fɔl]

Baby birds usually learn to fly when they fall out of their nest. As they are falling, they flap their wings and hope for the best!

雛鳥通常在從巢中掉下來時學會飛行。當牠們墜落時，會拍動翅膀，希望一切順利！

farm 農場 n. [fɑrm]

A farm is a piece of land to grow vegetables and fruit or to raise animals. Farms are very important because without farms, we would all go hungry!

農場是用來種植蔬菜、水果或飼養動物的土地。農場很重要，因為沒有農場，我們都會挨餓！

fat 肥胖；脂肪 n. [fæt]

Have you ever wondered how polar bears stay warm? Their thick fur helps, but they also have a thick layer of fat under their fur.

你有沒有想過北極熊是如何保暖的？牠們厚厚的皮毛有幫助，但皮毛下也有一層厚厚的脂肪。

feed 餵養 v. [fid]

Why do you think it is bad to feed animals human food?

為什麼你認為餵動物吃人類食物是不好的？

feel 覺得；感到 v. [fil]

Seals don't have fur, so how come they don't feel cold in icy water? Like polar bears, they have a thick layer of fat that helps keep them warm.

海豹沒有毛，為什麼牠們在冰水裡不覺得冷呢？像北極熊一樣，牠們有一層厚厚的脂肪，有助於保暖。

field 田野；牧場 n. [fild]

A field is a large place of open land. It is usually covered in grass or wheat. When you look at a field from far away, it doesn't seem like there would be a lot of wildlife, but if you take a magnifying glass, you will be able to see many interesting bugs and plants living in the dirt and grass.

田野是一大片廣闊的土地。它通常被草或小麥覆蓋著。當你從遠處看著一片田地時，似乎不會有很多野生動物，但如果你拿放大鏡，你會看到許多有趣的蟲子和植物生活在泥土和草地上。

fish 魚 n. [fɪʃ]

A fish breathes through it's gills. Gills are those lines on the sides of their heads that open and close. The gills take oxygen out of the water for the fish to breath. People need oxygen too, but we get oxygen from air instead of water.

魚是藉由鰓呼吸。鰓是牠們頭部兩側張開和閉合的線。鰓從水中吸取氧氣，讓魚呼吸。人們也需要氧氣，但我們是從空氣而不是水中獲得氧氣。

fix 修理 v. [fɪks]

What do you do when something breaks? Most kids ask their mom or dad to fix whatever is broken. But, why don't you try something new?

當東西壞了你會怎麼辦？無論是什麼壞了，大部分的小孩會請求他們的爸爸或媽媽來修理。不過，你何不嘗試些新方式呢？

flower 花 n [ˋflauɚ]

Flowers are very beautiful to
look at, but they are also very
important for bees. Bees will
take nectar and pollen from
flowers to bring home to make
honey.

花看起來很漂亮，對蜜蜂來說
也是很重要。蜜蜂會把花蜜和
花粉帶回家製造蜂蜜。

fly 飛翔 v. [flaɪ]

Most birds fly by flapping their wings.
Some birds, like hawks, soar.
This means, they open their
wings and let the wind
carry them from place to place.

大多數的鳥靠著振動翅膀來飛行。
有些鳥像鷹翱翔，也就是說，
牠們只要張開翅膀，讓風把牠們
從一個地方吹到另一個地方。

fox 狐狸 n. [fɑks]

Foxes have such good ears that they
can hear mice running underground.
This helps them hunt for food.

狐狸耳朵很好，能聽見老鼠在地下
跑。這有助於牠們覓食。

friend 朋友 n. [frɛnd]

Foxes are solitary animals. This means that they do not have friends and like to be by themselves.

狐狸是獨居的動物。這意味著牠們並沒有朋友，喜歡獨處。

frolic 嬉戲；打鬧 v. [`frɑlɪk]

Baby foxes like to frolic and play near their den. A den is an underground home. As soon as they hear or see something scary, they run underground into their den.

小狐狸喜歡在巢穴附近嬉戲玩耍。巢穴是一個地下的家。一旦他們聽到或看到一些可怕的事，牠們就會往地下的巢穴跑。

TRY IT

1. An _____ can weigh around 7,500 kilograms, making it the biggest land animal on earth.
   一頭大象重約7500公斤，是地球上最大的陸地動物。

2. _____ is the only planet that humans can live on.
   地球是人類唯一可以生存的星球。

3. It's important to control your _____. If you feel yourself getting angry, try taking a nap.
   控制情緒很重要。如果覺得自己很生氣，試著休息一下。

4. The bee took nectar from the _____ to bring back to its hive.
   蜜蜂從花上採蜜帶回蜂巢。

5. The polar bear needed more _____ on his body, so he went hunting for food.
   北極熊的身體需要更多的脂肪，因此去獵食。

6. I want to see the zookeeper _____ the baby giraffe food.
   我想要看動物飼養員餵長頸鹿寶寶吃東西。

Answer

1. elephant 2. Earth 3. emotions
4. flower 5. fat 6. feed

Gg

gain 獲得；取得 v. [gen]

How come when I eat one pound of food, I don't gain one pound of weight? Some of your food turns into energy. That energy is used to do things like walking, talking, running, and thinking.

為什麼當我吃一磅的食物，沒有增加一磅的體重？你吃的一些食物轉變成能量，這些能量被用來做如走路、說話、跑步和思考之類的事情。

game 遊戲 n. [gem]

Video games are fun, but they can be bad for your brain and memory. Instead of playing video games, try reading a book.

雖然電子遊戲很有趣，但它對你的大腦和記憶有壞處。與其玩電子遊戲，不如試著看書。

garden 花園 n. ['gardn]

A garden is a fascinating place to learn about nature. You can find worms, spiders, bees, and butterflies. All of these creatures are important to a garden. Without one, the plants in a garden will not grow as well.

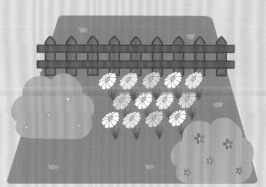

花園是個瞭解自然生態的有趣地方。你可以找到蠕蟲、蜘蛛、蜜蜂和蝴蝶。這些生物對花園都很重要。缺少任何一種，花園裡的植物就會長不好。

gas 氣；氣體 n. [gæs]

Helium is lighter than the air we breathe. Helium is a type of gas that is put into balloons to make them float.

氦氣比我們呼吸的空氣輕。氦氣是一種放進氣球中會使氣球漂浮的氣體。

get 得到 v. [gɛt]

Our body needs to get the right amount of sleep to work properly. Kids should sleep about 10 hours every day.

我們的身體需要足夠的睡眠才能夠正常地工作。小孩每天應該睡10個小時。

glove 手套（分手指的） n. [glʌv]

A long time ago, only rich people wore gloves. People with less money wore mittens.

很久以前，只有有錢人才戴得起分手指的手套。比較窮的人都是戴連指手套。

good 好的；令人滿意的 adj. [gʊd]

A good experiment should be interesting, important, and repeatable. If you cannot do the experiment over and over again, you won't know if the answer is good or not.

一個好的實驗應該是有趣的、重要的、可重複的。如果你不能一遍又一遍地做這個實驗，你就不知道答案是好還是壞。

grass 草 n. [græs]

Why does fresh cut grass smell so good? When grass is hurt it lets out a smell to let other plants know there is danger around.

為什麼剛割好的草聞起來這麼香？當草受到傷害時，它會散發出氣味，讓其他植物知道周圍有危險。

ground 地面 n. [graund]

If the ground is too cold, planted seeds won't grow. The temperature needs to be above 32 degrees Fahrenheit.

如果地面太冷，種下的種子無法生長。溫度必須在華氏三十二度以上。

grumpy 易怒、脾氣不好的 adj. [ˋgrʌmpɪ]

If you are waking up grumpy, it may be because you aren't getting enough sleep. Remember, your body needs about 10 hours of sleep every day.

如果你有起床氣，可能是因為你睡眠不足。記住，你的身體每天需要約十小時的睡眠時間。

Hh

happy 快樂的；幸福的 adj. [`hæpɪ]

When a dog is happy, it wags its tail.
When a cat is happy, it purrs and
meows. What do you do when you
are happy?

狗高興時會搖尾巴，當貓快樂時會發
出低沉的叫聲。當你感到快樂的時候
會有什麼反應呢？

haul 拖；拉 v. [hɔl]

Where does all the trash go?
A garbage truck hauls trash
to a landfill.

所有的垃圾都到哪裡去了？垃圾車
會將垃圾拖到垃圾掩埋場。

hay 乾草 n. [he]

Why are horses always chewing? Hay is very good for horses, but it is very hard and stiff. Horses chew on hay to soften it up before they swallow.

為什麼馬總是在嚼東西？乾草對馬非常好，但非常硬。馬在吞下乾草之前會先咀嚼讓乾草軟化。

head 頭部 n. [hɛd]

What is the difference between a mouse and a rat? Mice and rats live in similar places and eat similar things, but a mouse's head is much smaller a rat's head. A rat has a heavy body, but a mouse is teeny tiny.

老鼠和田鼠有什麼差別？老鼠和田鼠生活在相似的地方、吃類似的食物，但老鼠的頭比田鼠小很多。田鼠的身體很重，但老鼠很小。

hill 小山丘 n. [hɪl]

An ant hill is where ants build their homes. The top of the hill is usually the entrance of the ant hill.

蟻丘是螞蟻建造蟻窩的地方。小山丘的頂部通常是蟻丘的入口。

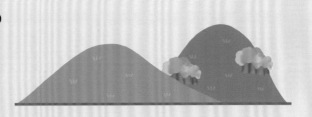

hobby 嗜好；業餘愛好 n. [ˋhɑbɪ]

Having a hobby is a good way to explore the world while making you smarter and stronger. I like to draw. What are your hobbies?

擁有嗜好是探索世界的好方法，同時使你變得更聰明、更強大。我喜歡畫畫。你的愛好是什麼？

honk 鵝叫 v. [hɔŋk]

Geese will honk when an intruder comes into their space. If a goose honks at you, step away!

當入侵者闖入鵝的活動範圍時，鵝會叫。如果一隻鵝對著你叫，離遠一點！

hop 單腳跳 v. [hɑp]

Bunnies hop instead of walk because their back legs are so long and strong.

兔子用跳的而不是用走的，是因為兔子的後腿又長又強壯。

horse 馬 n. [hɔrs]

Horses can sleep standing up. This is to help wild horses run away quickly when they hear a predator (a bad guy).

馬可以站著睡覺。這是為了幫助野馬在聽到掠食者（壞傢伙）的聲音時迅速逃跑。

hover 盤旋，翱翔 v. [ˋhʌvɚ]

A helicopter can hover in one place because the propeller pushes wind downward against the ground. This lifts the helicopter up.

直升機可以在一個地方盤旋，是因為螺旋槳將風向下推向地面，把直升機抬起來。

TRY IT

1. Fresh cut _____ smells so nice.
   剛割下來的草很好聞。

2. There are so many ladybugs in the _____. They help keep the flowers and plants safe.
   花園裡有很多瓢蟲。牠們有助於保護花草的安全。

3. Freezing water turns into a solid (ice). When water is in boiling temperatures, it turns into a _____.
   冰水變成固體（冰）。當水處於沸騰的溫度時，就會變成氣體。

4. _____ can eat hay, but humans cannot.
   馬可以吃乾草，但人不行。

5. When it feels scared, a rabbit will _____ away quickly.
   當兔子感到害怕時，會快速地跳走。

6. Those geese are _____ so loudly. I better not get too close.
   這群鵝叫聲很大，我最好不要太靠近牠們。

Answer

1. grass	2. garden	3. gas
4. Horses	5. hop	6. honking

Ii

ice 冰 n. [aɪs]

The ice in glaciers and ice sheets are quickly melting because of climate change. Climate change is when the earth gets warmer because of pollution. If the glaciers and ice sheets melt, animals like polar bears won't have a home.

由於氣候變遷，冰河和冰原中的冰正迅速融化。氣候變遷是因汙染讓地球暖化。如果冰河和冰原融化，像北極熊這樣的動物就沒有家了。

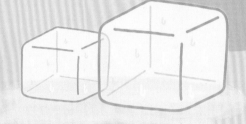

idea 意見；想法 n. [aɪˋdɪə]

What are some ideas that you have to help save the planet?

你有什麼想法來幫助維護地球？

46

imagine 想像；設想 v. [ɪˈmædʒɪn]

Imagine a world without any cute and cuddly panda bears. If we don't do our best to protect our planet, animals like panda bears will go extinct.

想像這個世界沒有可愛的熊貓。如果我們不盡力保護我們的地球，熊貓等動物將會絕種。

impolite 不禮貌的；粗魯的 adj. [ˌɪmpəˈlaɪt]

It is impolite to litter. Littering affects everyone around you.

亂丟垃圾是不禮貌的。亂丟垃圾會影響你周圍的每個人。

important 重要的；珍貴的 adj. [ɪmˋpɔrtnt]

It is important to reduce, reuse, and recycle plastic and glass. It takes one thousand years for a plastic bag to decompose.

塑膠和玻璃的減少、再利用及回收很重要。塑膠袋分解需要一千年的時間。

into 進入；到……裡面 prep. [ˋɪntu]

I got into trouble for throwing my plastic bottle in the trash.

因為我把寶特瓶丟進垃圾桶，惹上了麻煩。

in 在……內（裡面）prep. [ɪn]

If we don't do anything about pollution and litter, in a few years, beautiful creatures like turtles and dolphins might go extinct.

如果我們對污染和垃圾不採取任何措施，幾年之內，像海龜和海豚這樣美麗的動物可能會絕種。

insect 昆蟲 n. [ˋɪnsɛkt]

Insects can be annoying creatures, but the world needs them. Insects help pollinate plants and bring nutrients to soil.

昆蟲可能是令人討厭的生物，但世界需要牠們幫助植物授粉和帶給土壤養分。

ignore 忽視、忽略；不理會 v. [ɪgˋnor]

If we keep ignoring our pollution problem, one day, we may not have any clean air to breathe.

如果我們一直忽視污染的問題，總有一天，我們可能會呼吸不到任何乾淨的空氣。

Jj

jacket 夾克 n. [`dʒækɪt]

A jacket will help keep you warm by keeping your body heat close to you.

一件夾克可以讓你保持溫暖，使身體發熱。

jaguar 美洲豹 n. [`dʒægwɑr]

The jaguar is the third largest cat in the world. Can you think of two other wild cats that would be bigger?

美洲豹是世界上第三大的貓科動物。
你能想到另外兩種更大的貓科動物嗎？

jam 果醬 n. [dʒæm]

You can make jam by heating fruits like strawberries or blueberries in a pan until juices come out and then adding equal parts sugar.

你可以用平底鍋加熱草莓或藍莓等水果，
直到果汁出現後加入等量的糖，就可以製成果醬。

jar 罐子；廣口瓶 n. [dʒɑr]

When you are done making jam,
you can store it in a jar.

果醬製成後，你可以儲存在罐子裡。

jealous 忌妒的；吃醋的 adj. [ˋdʒɛləs]

Do you think jaguars are jealous of
tigers and lions for being bigger?

你認為美洲豹會嫉妒老虎和獅子的體型比較大嗎？

jog 慢跑 v. [dʒɑg]

Jogging is a great way to
make your heart stronger.

慢跑是個使你心臟更強壯的好方法。

join 參加 v. [dʒɔɪn]

Exercise is difficult, but it can be fun.
Try joining a sports team. Anything
that gets you moving is good for your
body and heart.

鍛鍊很困難，但也可以很有趣。試著加
入一個運動團隊。任何能讓你動起來的
事物對你的身體和心臟都有好處。

joy 歡欣；喜悅 n. [dʒɔɪ]

When you dance, your body creates a chemical that causes joy. So, next time you are feeling sad, try dancing!

跳舞時，你的身體會產生一種帶來喜悅的化學物質。所以下次你覺得難過時，試試跳舞吧！

jump 跳；跳躍 v. [dʒʌmp]

Jumping on a trampoline is also a way to exercise. It helps you with balance and it helps build muscles in the legs.

跳彈跳床也是一種鍛鍊的管道。它有助於你保持平衡，也有助於增強腿部肌肉。

jungle 叢林 n. [ˋdʒʌŋgl̩]

Jungles are like rainforests, but they have more sunlight and less trees.

叢林就像雨林，但陽光充足，樹木稀少。

TRY IT

1. The _____ got caught in the spider's web.
   昆蟲被蜘蛛網抓住了。

2. I found this plastic bottle _____ the garbage bin.
   我在垃圾桶裡發現了這個塑膠瓶。

3. When I walked _____ the kitchen, my mom got mad at me for throwing my trash in the recycling bin.
   當我走進廚房時，我媽媽因為我把垃圾丟進回收桶而生我的氣。

4. The top three largest wild cats are the lion, tiger, and _____.
   前三個最大的野生貓科動物分別是獅子、老虎和美洲豹。

5. Close the lid on the jam _____, please.
   請關上果醬罐的蓋子。

6. _____ are warm places with a lot of rainfall. Animals like jaguars live there.
   叢林是雨量充沛的溫暖地區，像美洲豹這樣的動物生活在那裡。

Answer

1. insect   2. in   3. into

4. jaguar   5. jar   6. Jungles

kangaroo 袋鼠 n. [ˌkæŋgəˋru]

The long tail of a kangaroo helps them balance when they are jumping.

袋鼠的長尾巴幫助牠們在
跳躍時保持平衡。

keep 保持；保存 v. [kip]

Songbirds keep their homes clean by throwing their chick's poops outside of the nest.

鳴禽把幼鳥的糞便扔到鳥巢
外，以保持家的乾淨。

key 鑰匙 n. [ki]

Thousands of years ago, people made keys with wood. The keys were so big, that only an adult could use them. Can you imagine using a key that big to open your door?

幾千年前,人們用木頭製作鑰匙。鑰匙大到只有成人能使用。你能想像用這麼大的鑰匙去開門嗎?

kick 踢;踹 v. [kɪk]

Kangaroos will kick their enemies with their large back legs. A kangaroo can really hurt you.

袋鼠會用牠們壯大的後腿踢敵人。袋鼠真的會傷害到你。

kid 小孩 n. [kɪd]

A human child is called a kid. Do you know of any animals that are called kids? Young dogs are called puppies. Young cats are called kittens.

人類的孩子被稱為小孩。你知道任何被稱為小孩的動物嗎?狗的小時候被稱為小狗。貓咪的小時候被稱為小貓。

king 國王 n. [kɪŋ]

King George became king when he was only 22 years old!

喬治國王成為國王時只有二十二歲！

kiss 吻；接吻 v. [kɪs]

There are no animals in the world that kiss. Dogs might lick your face to show that they like you, but it is not the same thing as a kiss.

世界上沒有動物會接吻。狗或許會舔你的臉來表示牠喜歡你，但這和接吻並不一樣。

kitchen 廚房 n. [ˋkɪtʃɪn]

You can try many different types of experiments with things found in your kitchen. Why do some foods turn brown when cooked? At what temperature does sugar melt? There is so much to discover!

你可以用廚房裡的東西做很多不同類型的試驗。為什麼有些食物在烹調時會變成咖啡色？糖在什麼溫度下會融化？你會有很多的發現！

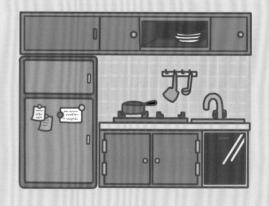

kite 風箏 n. [kaɪt]

The first kites that were ever invented were made in Asia.

最早發明的風箏是在亞洲製造的。

knock 敲打；擊 v. [nɑk]

Woodpeckers are very interesting birds. They are known for knocking on wood. Why do they do knock on wood? There are four big reasons why: They are carving out a home in the wood, they are eating bugs they find on the wood, they are making a hole to hide their food, or they want other birds to know "I'M HERE."

啄木鳥是非常有趣的鳥。牠們以敲打木頭而聞名。牠們為什麼會敲木頭？有四大原因：牠們正在木頭上雕刻房屋、正在吃在木頭上發現的蟲子、正在挖洞來藏食物，或者牠們想讓其他鳥知道"我在這裡"。

Ll

ladybug 瓢蟲 n. [ˋledɪˏbʌɡ]

Ladybugs are not only beautiful, they are also great friends of gardeners. They help eat all the bad bugs that eat flowers and plants.

瓢蟲不僅漂亮，而且是園丁的好朋友。牠們會幫忙把所有吃花和植物的壞蟲吃掉。

lake 湖泊 n. [lek]

Lakes and ponds are bodies of water that do not flow anywhere. A lake is like a big pond.

湖泊和池塘都是不流動的水域。湖就是一個大池塘。

land 陸地 n. [lænd]

Earth has more water than land. Only about 30 percent of earth is land. The rest is water!

地球上的水比陸地多。地球只有百分之三十是陸地，剩下的都是水！

late 晚期的 adj. / adv. [let]

It's never too late to learn. A 95-year-old woman graduated from college and is one of the oldest college graduates.

活到老學到老。一個九十五歲的婦人從大學畢業，也是最年長的畢業生之一。

leaf 葉子；樹葉 n. [lif]

In the fall, because there is less daylight and the temperature gets colder, trees stop sending food to leaves. A leaf will turn from green to yellow. Then, it falls off the tree.

秋天因為日光較少和溫度變低，樹停止輸送養分至樹葉。葉子會由綠色變黃色，然後從樹上掉下來。

left 左邊（側）的 adj. [lɛft]

If you have trouble remembering which way is left and which way is right, make an "L" shape with your finger and thumb. If the letter is backwards, that's your right hand. If it looks like an "L," that's your left hand.

如果你左右不分，用你的手指和拇指做一個 "L" 形。如果字母相反，那是你的右手。如果它看起來像 "L"，那是你的左手。

leg 腿部 adj. [lɛg]

A giraffe's legs are taller than most adults! Their long legs let them run very fast.

長頸鹿的腿比大多數成年人高！牠們的長腿讓牠們跑得很快。

lend 借出 v. [lɛnd]

Reading helps us learn all about the world comfortably from home. The library will lend out books for weeks so that you can take your time reading.

我們可以在家舒服地閱讀來瞭解世界。圖書館的書可以借幾週，這樣你可以慢慢看書。

lion 獅子 n. [ˋlaɪən]

Lions like to roar as soon as they wake up to let other lions know, "I'm here. Stay away! "

獅子一睡醒喜歡吼叫，讓其他獅子知道 "我在這裡離我遠一點！"

listen 聆聽 v. [ˋlɪsn̩]

Have you ever noticed that it is never completely quiet? If you close your eyes and listen, you will hear many different noises, even when you think it's quiet.

你是否曾經注意到，從來沒有完全安靜的時刻？如果你閉上眼睛聆聽，你會聽到許多不同的聲音，即使你認為很安靜。

love 愛 n. [lʌv]

Where does love come from? Where do you feel love? Do you feel it in your brain or in your heart? Do you think animals can feel love?

愛從何而來？你在哪裡感受得到愛？在你的大腦或是心裡感覺得到嗎？你認為動物可以感受到愛嗎？

TRY IT

1. Try to _____ a notebook and pencil with you at all times. That way, if you think of an idea or a question, you can write it down and save it for later.

   試著隨身攜帶筆記本和鉛筆。這樣如果你有想法或問題時，可以記錄下來留到以後使用。

2. If you lose your _____, you can call a locksmith to help you open the lock.

   如果你遺失了鑰匙，你可以叫鎖匠幫你開鎖。

3. A kangaroo can _____ very hard, but a zebra has an even stronger _____.

   袋鼠可以踢得很大力，但斑馬可以踢得更大力。

4. I know it is fall when the _____ start to turn from green to yellow.

   我知道當樹葉開始從綠色變成黃色時，就是秋天了。

5. I _____ my friends, but I _____ my family.

   我喜歡我的朋友，但我愛我的家人。

6. You should always _____ to your parents because they know you best.

   你應該常聽你父母的話，因為他們最瞭解你。

Answer

1. keep	2. key	3. kick (v.), kick (n.)
4. leaves	5. like, love	6. listen

Mm

machine 機器；機械裝置 n. [mə`ʃin]

An engineer is someone whose job is to make and design machines. These machines can be robots, tools, computers, or any other thing that has a function. They can also be simple things like shovels, wheel barrows, and bicycles.

工程師是負責製造和設計機器的人。這些機器可以是機器人、工具、電腦或其他任何具有某種功能的東西。它們也可以是簡單的東西，像鏟子、手推車和腳踏車。

mad 生氣的；憤怒的 adj. [mæd]

When we get mad, our heartbeats get faster. This causes a lot of stress that is bad for the body, so whenever you are feeling angry, close your eyes and breathe.

當我們生氣時，我們的心跳會加快。這會對身體造成很大的有害壓力，所以每當你感到憤怒時，閉上眼睛深呼吸。

mailbox 郵筒；信箱 n. [ˋmelˌbɑks]

When you have finished writing a letter, you can put it in an envelope with a stamp and address, then stick it in a mailbox. The mailman will come and get it and help you deliver it.

當你寫完一封信後，你可以把它放進一個貼好郵票和寫好地址的信封裡，然後放進郵桶內。郵差會過來取走，幫你寄送。

make 做；製造 v. [mek]

Did you know that some animals can understand your facial expressions? If you make a happy face, the dog may wag its tail.

你知道有些動物能夠瞭解你的臉部表情嗎？如果你做一個快樂的表情，狗可能會搖尾巴。

maybe 或許；大概 adv. [ˋmebɪ]

Try reading a book. Maybe you will learn something new.

試著看一本書，也許你能夠學到新的東西。

mean 兇惡的 adj. [min]

Small dogs sometimes seem mean; They may show their teeth and growl, but usually, this is because they are scared. You are much bigger, and the small dog needs to protect itself. So next time you see a small dog, go up to it slowly and gently.

小狗有時看起來很兇惡；牠們可能會露出牙齒咆哮，但這通常是因為害怕。你比狗還大，小狗需要保護自己。所以下次你看到一隻小狗時，慢慢地、輕輕地靠近牠。

meet 見面；相識 v. [mit]

Have you ever met a dolphin? Dolphins are very curious creatures and love to say hello to people who are close by.

你見過海豚嗎？海豚是非常好奇的生物，喜歡和身邊的人打招呼。

milk 牛奶 n. [mɪlk]

When a baby is born, it needs to drink its mother's milk right away because the milk has vitamins and other good things that help protect the baby from germs.

嬰兒出生後，需要立即喝母乳，因為母乳含有維生素和其他有助於保護嬰兒免受細菌感染的好東西。

mountain 山脈 n. [ˈmauntn̩]

The world's highest mountain is called Mount Everest. It takes about two months to get to the top by foot.

世界上最高的山叫做珠穆朗瑪峰。步行到山頂大約需要兩個月的時間。

mouse 老鼠 n. [maus]

Because mice can't see very well, a mouse uses its whiskers and ears to move around.

因為老鼠的視力不好，所以是靠牠的鬍鬚和耳朵移動。

muscle 肌肉 n. [ˋmʌsļ]

You need to eat healthy food and exercise to grow your muscles and become strong.

你需要吃健康的食物並鍛鍊身體來增長肌肉變強壯。

mushroom 蘑菇 n. [ˋmʌʃrum]

When you cook mushrooms, they shrink because all the water comes out.

在你煮蘑菇時，它會縮小是因為所有的水分跑出來了。

歡迎來到小遊戲時間，請爸爸、媽媽與小朋友一起來玩Bingo吧，一人拿出一張紙在紙上畫出直線3條、橫線3條共9格的Bingo卡，選定之前出現的一個單字隨機填進格子中，率先連到2條線的人就獲勝！

Nn

nap 小睡；打盹 v. [næp]

Taking a nap can help you think, be creative, and be happier. Some scientists say that it is best to nap for twenty minutes. If you're feeling sleepy, go ahead and take a nap.

小睡可以幫助你思考，讓你更有創造力、更快樂。一些科學家說，二十分鐘是最恰當的小睡時間。如果你覺得睏了，就去睡一覺吧。

nature 大自然 n. [ˋnetʃɚ]

When you have time, take a walk through nature. It will help you relax and is good exercise.

當你有時間的時候，在大自然中散步。能幫助你放鬆，也是很好的鍛鍊。

need 必須；需要 v. [nid]

When you were a baby, you needed an adult to help keep you safe, feed you, and take care of you. Baby sea turtles are very different. The mother turtle lays her eggs and then leaves the eggs by themselves. When the baby sea turtles are born, they have to live all on their own.

當你還是嬰兒時，你需要成年人保護你的安全，養育你，照顧你。小海龜很不一樣。海龜媽媽產完卵就會離開。小海龜出生後必須獨自生活。

net 網子 n. [nɛt]

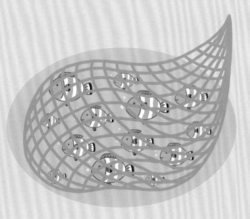

A fishing net is used for fishing. Fishermen can use a fishing pole to catch one fish and a net to catch many fish.

漁網是用來捕魚的。
漁夫可以用魚竿釣一條魚，
用網子抓很多魚。

new 新的 adj. [nju]

How do you learn new things? You can learn new things from your parents, teachers, and friends. You can also learn new facts from books or from experiments.

你如何學習新的事物？你可以請教你的父母、老師和朋友。你也可以從書本或實驗中學習新的事實。

nibble 咬；啃 v. [ˋnɪbl̩]

When a fisherman uses a fishing pole, he throws the line with a hook into the water. When a fish nibbles on the food at the end of the hook, the line will wiggle, and the fisherman will know he's caught a fish.

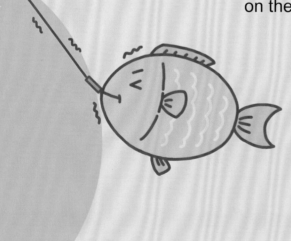

當漁夫使用釣竿時，他把綁有魚鉤的釣線拋進水裡。當一條魚咬住魚鉤末端的食物時，釣線就會擺動，漁夫就會知道他釣到一條魚了。

noisily 吵雜地 adv. [ˋnɔɪzɪlɪ]

Animals and insects are always
noisily buzzing, humming, chirping,
squawking, grunting, and howling.
That's why jungles are so noisy.
There are many animals and they
all try to talk to each other, scare
other creatures, or warn their
friends.

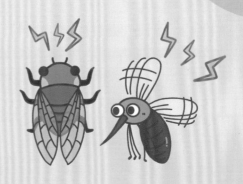

動物和昆蟲總是吵雜地嗡嗡作響、唧唧叫、
咯咯叫、呼嚕叫、嗥叫，這就是叢林如此喧
鬧的原因。有許多動物都試圖互相交談，嚇
唬其他動物，或警告牠們的朋友。

noisy 喧鬧的；吵雜的 adj. [ˋnɔɪzɪ]

Pollution is when something goes into the
environment and is harmful to
the earth, people, and animals
in that environment. Usually this is
something like gas from a car, but it can
also be something like noise.
Noise pollution is when an
area is always noisy.
It hurts your ears and
stresses animals out.

污染是指有東西進入
環境，對環境中的地球、人和動物有害。
通常像是汽車排放的氣體，但也可像是噪
音。噪音汙染是指一個地區總是很喧鬧。
它會傷害你的耳朵並讓動物感到緊張。

nose 鼻子 n. [noz]

A shark's nose can smell blood from half a kilometer away. Unlike people, sharks don't use their nose to breathe. They only use their nose to smell.

鯊魚的鼻子可以聞到半公里外的血腥味。與人不同，鯊魚不是用鼻子呼吸，只是用鼻子聞東西。

TRY IT

1. You can _____ butter by pouring a heavy milk (like whipping cream) into a jar and shaking the jar for about fifteen minutes.
   你可以把生奶油（像鮮奶油）倒進罐子裡搖十五分鐘來製成奶油。

2. The _____ used his big ears to listen for the cat. When the cat was gone, he ran into the kitchen and stole some cheese.
   老鼠用牠的大耳朵來聽貓在哪裡。當貓不在時，就會跑進廚房偷起司。

3. I exercise every day so that my _____ can grow strong.
   我每天鍛鍊身體，這樣我的肌肉才會變得結實。

4. We can learn _____ things through experiments, books, or asking other people.
   我們可以透過實驗、書籍，或詢問他人來學到新的事物。

5. Forests can be very _____ at night with all the nocturnal (night) animals making noises.
   夜間的森林會非常吵雜，所有夜間活動的動物都會發出噪音。

6. I am so tired. I need to take a _____.
   我太累了。我需要小睡一會兒。

Answer

1. make	2. mouse	3. muscles
4. new	5. noisy	6. nap

ocean 海洋 n. [ˈoʃən]

The youngest person to sail around the world was only sixteen years old. It took her almost two years of sailing through oceans (the Arctic, Atlantic, Indian, Pacific, and Southern) to get back home. She did it all by herself. Would you be scared to sail in a boat by yourself for two years?

環遊世界最年輕的人只有十六歲。她花了近兩年的時間在海洋中航行（北極海、大西洋、印度洋、太平洋、南大洋）才回到家。她自己做到了這一切。你會害怕自己獨自乘船航行兩年嗎？

odd 奇數的；單數的 adj. [ɑd]

An even number will end in 0,2,4,6, or 8. An odd number will end in 1, 3, 5, 7, or 9.

偶數會以 0、2、4、6 或 8 結尾。
奇數會以 1、3、5、7 或 9 結尾。

off 離開；遠離 prep. [ɔf]

A long time ago, people thought the world was flat and if you sailed a boat too far, you would fall off the side of earth!

很久以前，人們認為世界是平坦的，如果你把船開得太遠，你就會從地球的另一邊掉下去！

oil 油 n. [ɔil]

No matter how much you try, oil and water won't mix together unless you use something called an emulsifier. An emulsifier helps two things stick.

無論你怎麼嘗試，油和水不會混合，除非使用一種稱為乳化劑的東西。乳化劑有助於將兩樣東西粘在一起。

once 一次；一回 adv. [wʌns]

Penguins migrate once a year. They migrate (move from one area to another area) to find food and start a family.

企鵝一年遷徙一次。牠們遷徙（從一個地區搬移到另一個地區）是為了覓食和組織家庭。

onion 洋蔥 n. [ˋʌnjən]

When you cut an onion, your eyes might start to water. This is because when the onion is cut, it lets go of an oil that turns into a gas. When the gas touches your eyes, your brain tells your eyes to cry to help push the gas away.

當你切洋蔥時，你的眼睛可能會開始流淚。這是因為當洋蔥被切下時，它會釋放出一種油，這種油會變成氣體。當氣體接觸到你的眼睛時，你的大腦會促使你哭來幫助氣體排開。

only 只；僅 adv. [ˋonlɪ]

There are only eighty Sumatran rhinos left in the wild. If we don't do anything to protect them, they will be extinct soon.

野生的蘇門答臘犀牛只剩下八十隻，如果我們不採取任何措施來保護牠們，牠們很快就會滅絕。

open 打開 v. [`opən]

Why is it easier to open a jar after you put it in hot water? When the metal lid gets warm or hot, it will get bigger. You might not be able to see it getting bigger, but it is.

為什麼你把罐子放進熱水裡後更容易打開？當金屬蓋升溫或變熱時，它會膨脹。你可能看不到它變大，但它確實是。

orange 橙；橘；柑 n. [`ɔrɪndʒ]

There is a type of orange called a Bergamot orange. It is not used for food, but the oil is used to clean germs and as a perfume.

有一種叫做香檸檬的柑橘。它不是用來做食物，但油用來清潔細菌和做香水。

ostrich 鴕鳥 n. [ˋɑstrɪtʃ]

In cartoons, you may see ostriches burying their heads in the ground, but in real life, they don't do this. They do dig holes to lay eggs. Then, they stick their heads in the hole to turn the eggs.

在卡通中，你可能會看到鴕鳥把頭埋進地底，但在現實生活中，牠們不會這樣做。牠們確實會挖洞產卵。然後把頭伸進洞裡轉動蛋。

owl 貓頭鷹 n. [aul]

Owls are nocturnal animals (Do you remember what nocturnal means? They are awake at night.) Owls have large eyes so they can see better at night.

貓頭鷹是夜行性動物（你還記得夜行性動物的意思嗎？牠們整晚都是醒著的。）貓頭鷹有雙大眼睛，所以牠們晚上能看得更清楚。

Pp

pad （能一張一張扯用的）便條紙簿 n. [pæd]

It is always a great idea to bring a pad of paper
and a pen with you wherever you go. This way
you can write down ideas,
questions, or stories wherever
you are, whenever you want.

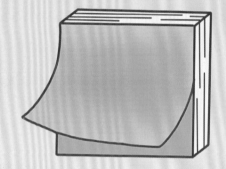

無論你去哪裡，隨身帶一本便條
簿和一支筆是個好主意。這樣你
就可以隨時隨地寫下想法、問題
或是故事。

paddle 用槳划船；撥水 v. [ˋpædl̩]

When a four-legged animal like a
dog, or a cat swim, they paddle
through water with their paws.
Most animals know how to paddle
without having to be taught.

當四隻腳的動物像狗或貓游泳時，
牠們會用爪子撥水。大部分的動物
不用教牠們就知道如何划水。

paint 繪畫 v. [pent]

Painting is a great way to express yourself.

繪畫是抒發自己的一種好方法。

painting 畫 [ˋpentɪŋ]

The oldest painting that humans have found is a cave painting. It is 64,000 years old and made by cavemen.

人類發現的最古老的畫是一幅洞穴壁畫。它有六萬四千年的歷史，是由穴居人製成。

pen 筆 n. [pɛn]

Pens used to be made of feathers. Nowadays, pens have ink inside of them but a long time ago, people would dip the tip of a feather into a bottle of ink, then use that to write. When there was no more ink on the feather, they would dip the feather into the ink again.

筆以前是用羽毛做的。如今，筆裡面有墨水，但很久以前，人們會把一根羽毛的尖端浸入一瓶墨水中，然後用它寫字。當羽毛上沒有墨水時，他們會把羽毛再放進墨水裡。

pencil 鉛筆 n. [ˋpɛnsl̩]

About 2,500 pencils can be made from one regular sized tree. In 1858, an American put an eraser at the end of a pencil for the first time.

大約兩千五百支鉛筆可以由一棵普通大小的樹製成。西元1858年，一位美國人第一次在鉛筆的末端放一塊橡皮擦。

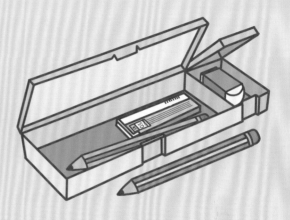

penguin 企鵝 n. [ˋpɛngwɪn]

Penguins are birds, but they can't fly! They are super cute when they waddle across the ice.

企鵝是鳥，但牠們不會飛！牠們搖搖晃晃地走在冰上時非常可愛。

pole 竿子；柱子 n. [pol]

When your fishing pole wiggles,
it means you have caught a fish!

當你的魚竿擺動時，代表你釣到
一條魚了！

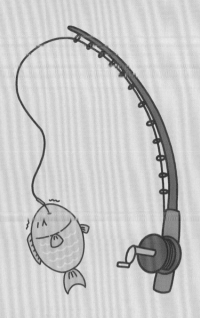

prefer 更喜愛；寧可 v. [prɪ`fɝ]

Do you prefer to learn
about science or learn
mathematics?

你比較喜歡學科學
還是學數學？

protect 保護；防護 v. [prə`tɛkt]

A kangaroo will carry its
joey (young kangaroo) in its
front pouch to protect it from
predators.

袋鼠會把牠的幼袋鼠放在牠的
前袋裡，以保護牠不受捕食者
的侵害。

pumpkin 南瓜 n. [ˋpʌmpkɪn]

Did you know that you can eat the flowers that grow out of a pumpkin? You can also eat the actual pumpkin. It is super good for you!

你知道你可以吃南瓜長出來的花嗎？你也可以吃真正的南瓜。對你有大有益處！

purple 紫色 n. [ˋpɝpɪ]

Purple grapes are actually better for you than green grapes. This is because the purple grape has more antioxidants. An antioxidant is kind of like a vitamin that helps protects your body.

其實紫葡萄比綠葡萄對你更好。是因為紫葡萄含有更多的抗氧化劑。抗氧化劑就像是一種維生素，有助於維持你身體的健康。

TRY IT

1. There are five _____ in the world: the Arctic, Atlantic, Indian, Pacific, and Southern.

   世界上有五大海洋，分別是北極海、大西洋、印度洋、太平洋和南大洋。

2. If you can't _____ a jar, you can put it in some hot water. It will be much easier to open this way!

   如果你罐子打不開，你可以把它放進熱水裡。這樣會更容易打開！

3. _____ and water can't mix together.

   油和水不能混合在一起。

4. _____ are great swimmers but can't fly. What a weird bird!

   企鵝是游泳健將，但不會飛。多麼奇怪的鳥！

5. My dog _____ towards me in the swimming pool.

   我的狗在游泳池裡向我游過來。

6. The cat stayed close to its kitten to _____ it from any predators.

   貓緊靠著牠的小貓來保護牠不受任何捕食性動物傷害。

Answer

1. oceans	2. open	3. Oil
4. Penguins	5. paddled	6. protect

84

Qq

quality 優質的 adj. [ˈkwɑlətɪ]

Beavers are very good at making quality dams. If a dam is not of good quality, water will push it over and destroy the home.

海狸非常擅長製造優質的水壩。如果水壩的品質不好，水就會推倒水壩並破壞房屋。

quarter 四分之一 n. [ˈkwɔrtɚ]

A quarter is half of a half of one.

四分之一是一半的一半。

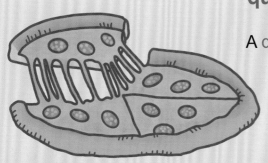

queasy 想吐的；噁心的 adj. [ˋkwizɪ]

Do you ever feel queasy on a boat?
Most people are not used to the back-
and-forth feeling of being on a boat.
Dizziness, that sick feeling is because
the liquid in your inner ear moves around
in a way that you are not used to. The
longer you stay on the boat, the more
you will get used to it.

你曾經在船上感到噁心嗎？
大多數人不習慣在船上搖晃
的感覺。頭暈，那種噁心的
感覺是因為你內耳的液體以
一種你不習慣的方式流動。
你在船上待得越久，就會越
習慣它。

queen 女王；蜂王 n. [ˋkwin]

Every beehive has one queen.
The queen is usually the biggest
bee and is in charge of laying lots
of eggs.

每個蜂巢都有一個女王蜂。
女王蜂通常是最大的蜜蜂，
負責產許多卵。

question 問題 n. [ˋkwɛstʃən]

Do you have a question? Don't be afraid to ask your teacher or parents!

你有什麼問題嗎？不要害怕去問你的老師或父母！

quick 快速的；短暫的 adj. [kwɪk]

A fox is quite quick. If a bird, like a chicken, isn't paying attention, a quick fox will quickly run over and grab one of its eggs.

狐狸的動作相當地快。如果鳥類，像是雞，一不注意，敏捷的狐狸會很快地跑過去抓一個雞蛋。

quiet 安靜的 adj. [ˋkwaɪət]

If you would like to do something peaceful, try going for a quiet walk through the forest.

如果你想做些平靜的事，試著在森林裡安靜的散步。

quit 放棄；停止 v. [kwɪt]

When it comes to starting
a family, penguins are very
stubborn. A male penguin will
look for the perfect rock to give to
a female penguin as a gift.
It will not quit until it finds the
perfect rock.

說到建立家庭，企鵝很固執。雄
性企鵝會尋找完美的石頭當作禮
物送給雌性企鵝。直到牠找到完
美的石頭，牠不會放棄。

quite 相當，很 adv. [kwaɪt]

Taiwan's 101 is quite tall, but
there are about 10 buildings that
are even taller than the 101.

台灣的101相當高，但大約有十棟
建築比101還要高。

rain 下雨 v. [ren]

Did you know that it rains on other planets in our Solar System? On earth, it rains water and sometimes hail (frozen water). Some scientists believe that it rains diamonds on Saturn, Neptune, and Jupiter!

你知不知道太陽系中的其他行星都會下雨？在地球會下雨，有時下冰雹（結凍的水）。一些科學家認為土星、海王星、木星會下鑽石雨！

read 閱讀 v. [rid]

The more you read, the more you'll know. Reading is a lot of fun. What is your favorite book?

你讀得越多，就知道得越多。閱讀很有趣。你最喜歡的書是什麼？

red 紅色 adj. [rɛd]

Red is a primary color. Green and blue are also primary colors. It is also the first color in a rainbow.

紅色是原色。綠色和藍色也是原色。紅色也是彩虹中的第一種顏色。

rest 休息；使……停止 v. [rɛst]

Giraffes rest for five minutes at a time and sleep only 30 minutes in total a day.

長頸鹿一次休息五分鐘，一天總共只睡三十分鐘。

right 右側的；正確的 adj. [raɪt]

The human brain has two parts: a left side and a right side. The left side of your brain helps control the right side of your body, and the right side of your brain helps control the left side of your body.

人的大腦有兩個部分：左腦和右腦。大腦的左側幫助你控制身體的右側，而大腦的右側幫助你控制身體的左側。

rise 上升；升起 v. [raɪz]

An ocean tide rises and falls depending on the moon. Weird, right? The moon has a pull that makes the water of an ocean go up or go down.

海洋的漲潮與退潮取決於月亮。很奇怪，對吧？月球有一種引力，使海洋的水上升或下降。

river 河流；水道 n. [ˋrɪvɚ]

Rivers are very powerful bodies of water. They can carve out valleys and canyons.

河流是非常強大的水體。它們可以開闢山谷和峽谷。

rocket 火箭 n. [ˋrɑkɪt]

In 1948, a monkey named Laika became the first animal that visited space in a rocket ship.

在1948年，一隻名叫萊卡的猴子成為第一隻坐火箭造訪太空的動物。

rooster 公雞 n. [ˋrustɚ]

A female chicken is called a hen, and a male chicken is called a rooster.

雌性的雞叫母雞，雄性的雞叫公雞。

rumble 轟隆作響 v. [ˋrʌmbḷ]

A herd of animals is a group of one type of animal. Cows, horses, and wildebeests are animals that live in herds. Some herds are so big and powerful that when they run, they make the ground rumble. When they run together, it is called a stampede.

群居動物是一種動物構成的團體。牛、馬和牛羚都是群居動物。有些獸群又大又強壯，奔跑時會使地面轟隆作響。當牠們一起跑的時候，稱為奔逃（指獸群或人群因恐懼引發的狂奔）

TRY IT

1. Does anyone have any _____?
   有人有任何問題嗎？

2. That bee is very big. It must be the _____.
   那隻蜜蜂很大。牠一定是女王蜂

3. The fox ran away _____ with a stolen egg.
   狐狸帶著偷來的蛋迅速地逃跑了。

4. The colors of a rainbow are _____, orange, yellow, green, blue, and violet.
   彩虹的顏色有紅色、橙色、黃色、綠色、藍色和紫色。

5. The ocean will _____ once a day.
   海洋每天會漲潮一次。

6. _____ have bright feathers and a red comb on top of its head. In the morning, it will crow to let other birds know it is awake.
   公雞有鮮艷的羽毛，頭頂有紅色的雞冠。牠早上會啼叫，讓其他小鳥知道牠醒了。

Answer

1. questions	2. queen	3. quickly
4. red	5. rise	6. Roosters

Ss

say 說 v [se]

Parrots can learn to speak.
Some parrots have learned how
to say over 100 English words!

鸚鵡可以學會說話。有些鸚鵡已
經學會說一百多個英文單字！

see 看 v. [si]

Eagles can see an animal from
three miles away.

老鷹可以看到三英里外的動物。

94

shell 貝殼；殼 n. [ʃɛl]

A shell is used to keep the creature inside safe. When a hermit crab grows too big, it will find a bigger shell to move into.

貝殼是用來保護殼內生物的安全。當寄居蟹長得太大時，牠會移居到一個更大的殼。

silver 銀 n. [ˈsɪlvɚ]

Silver feels very hard in our hands, but it's actually a soft metal. People will usually mix it with other metals to make it harder.

銀在我們手中感覺很硬，但它實際上是種軟金屬。人們通常把銀和其他金屬混合，讓它變得更硬。

sit 坐；坐下 v. [sɪt]

It is not good for your body to sit for too long. If you see your mom or dad sitting for too long, tell them to get up and stretch!

坐著太久對你身體不好。
如果你看到父母長時間坐著，告訴他們起來伸展一下！

95

snake 蛇 n. [snek]

A snake will eat a mouse in one bite. Sometimes you can see the mouse it has just swallowed going down its body.

蛇能一口吃掉老鼠。有時你可以看到剛被蛇吞進肚子裡的老鼠順著牠的身體向下移動。

sneak 潛行；偷偷地走 v. [snik]

A lioness will sneak through grass behind its prey. When it gets close enough, it jumps out and kills its prey.

母獅會偷偷地穿過獵物後面的草，當牠距離夠近時，會跳出來殺死獵物。

snow 下雪 v. [sno]

Antarctica is one of the coldest places on earth, but surprisingly, there is one area called The Dry Valleys where it has never snowed.

南極洲是地球上最冷的地方之一，但令人驚訝的是，有一個叫乾旱谷的地區從未下過雪。

soar 飛翔；驟升 v. [sor]

A flying squirrel is a special type of squirrel that has extra skin that connects their hands and feet. This helps them soar through the sky from tree to tree.

飛鼠是一種特殊的松鼠，有額外的皮膚連接著牠們的手和腳。這幫助牠們在樹與樹之間的空中飛翔。

splash 濺；灑 v. [splæʃ]

Whales will splash water with their tail to scare fish to the surface. They also do this as a way to talk to other whales.

鯨魚會用尾巴濺水，把魚嚇到水面。牠們這樣做也是和其他鯨魚交談的一種方式。

stand 站立 v. [stænd]

Many animals sleep standing up. Elephants, horses, zebras, and flamingos all sleep standing up. Flamingos sleep standing up because there is nowhere to sit or lay down.

許多動物站著睡覺。大象、馬、斑馬和紅鶴都是站著睡覺。紅鶴站著睡覺是因為沒有地方可以坐下或躺下。

stripe 條紋；斑紋 n. [straɪp]

A zebra's stripes help them
blend into their environment.
Their stripes are used as
camouflage, so predators have
a hard time seeing them.

斑馬的條紋有助於融入環境。
牠們的條紋用來偽裝，所以捕
食者很難看到牠們。

sun 太陽；陽光 n. [sʌn]

The bright sun is very old.
It's 4,500,000,000 years old! Without the
sun, nothing on earth would exist!
We all need the power, warmth,
and light of the sun.

明亮的太陽很老，它有四十五億年的歷史。
沒有太陽，地球上什麼都不會存活！
我們需要太陽的能量、溫暖和照明！

swim 游泳 v. [swɪm]

A diver is a person who swims deep
into the ocean. Divers usually wear an
oxygen tank that lets them breathe,
a wetsuit that keeps them warm, and
flippers to help swim faster.

潛水員是指在海洋深處游泳的人。潛
水員通常會戴上氧氣瓶讓他們呼吸，
穿潛水衣保暖，以及穿上蛙鞋讓他們
游得更快。

Tt

take 拿；奪取 v. [tek]

Hyena's are sneaky animals that will take food from other animals when they aren't watching.

鬣狗是一種偷偷摸摸的動物，牠們會趁其他動物不注意時，拿走食物。

tea 茶；茶葉 n. [ti]

Tea is made by soaking the leaves of a tea in hot water. People all over the world drink tea, but it first came from Asia.

茶是用熱水浸泡茶葉製成的。全世界的人都喝茶，但茶是源自於亞洲。

99

teacher 老師；教職員 n. [ˈtitʃɚ]

Teachers can help you learn.

老師可以幫助你學習。

tickle 搔癢 v. [ˈtɪkl̩]

When humans are tickled, they usually laugh. Animals are ticklish too! Scientists have studied some animals and have proven that when you tickle them, they will laugh or move around. Are you ticklish?

當人被搔癢時，他們通常會笑。動物也怕癢！科學家們研究了一些動物，證明了當你搔動物癢時，牠們會笑或是到處走動。你會怕癢嗎？

tiger 老虎 n. [ˈtaɪgɚ]

Tigers are the largest wild cats in the world. They need to eat a lot of meat to take care of their big bodies.

老虎是世界上最大的野貓。牠們需要吃很多的肉來照顧牠們的大身體。

time 時間 n. [taɪm]

A sundial is a way to use the sun
to tell the time. A sundial
has a pointer sticking up in the
center. The sun will cast
a shadow on this pointer
and wherever the shadow
is pointing is what time it is.

日晷是一種利用太陽來判
斷時間的方法。日晷的中
心有一個指針。太陽會在
指針上投下陰影，陰影指
向的地方就是時間。

tiny 極小的；微小的 adj. [ˋtaɪnɪ]

The world's tiniest animal is
a frog called a Paedophryne
amauensis. It is half the size of
an American penny!

世界上最小的動物是一種叫做
阿馬烏童蛙的青蛙。牠的體型是
美金硬幣一分錢的一半！

tired 累的；疲倦的 adj. [taɪrd]

Dolphins half sleep, yet they don't get tired. They close one eye and let half their brain and body rest while the other side stays awake. This way, they can half-sleep and still stay safe from predators.

海豚半睡半醒，但牠們並不累。牠們閉一隻眼，讓一半的大腦和身體休息，而另一半保持清醒。這樣一來，牠們可以在半睡眠狀態下仍不受掠食者傷害。

tree 樹木 n. [tri]

The roots of a tree will soak up water and nutrients to help the tree grow. A strong tree will release oxygen. People need oxygen to breathe.

樹根會吸收水分和養分，幫助樹木生長。強壯的樹會釋放氧氣。人們需要氧氣來呼吸。

truck 卡車；貨車 n. [trʌk]

Most trucks use a special type of fuel called diesel gas. Because trucks are so big and heavy, they need more power. A diesel engine is much more powerful than the engine in a regular car. Diesel gas helps power a diesel engine.

大多數的卡車使用一種叫做柴油的特殊燃料。因為卡車又大又重，需要更多的動力。柴油引擎的動力比一般汽車引擎大。柴油會促使柴油引擎發動。

turtle 烏龜 n. [ˋtɝtḷ]

Turtles are known to be slow animals, but once you put a sea turtle in water, it can swim pretty fast!

眾所皆知，烏龜是動作很慢的動物，可是一旦你把海龜放進水裡，牠可以游得很快！

TRY IT

1. Elephants are surprisingly good swimmers. Even though they are very big, they can _____ very fast and can float easily.

   大象出人意外地很意外的善於游泳。即使牠們體型很大，也可以游得很快、輕鬆的漂浮。

2. The predator is _____ behind its prey.

   捕食者正偷偷地躲在獵物後面。

3. Your plant needs more light. You should put it outside under the _____.

   你的植物需要更多的光。你應該把它放在外面的陽光下。

4. That squirrel _____ a peanut right out of my hand!

   那隻松鼠從我手中拿走一顆花生！

5. Many animals live in the branches and trunk of a _____. The leaves help protect the animals from predators and from the sun.

   許多動物生活在樹枝和樹幹上。葉子有助於保護動物不受掠食者的傷害和太陽的照射。

6. A _____ has a hard shell on its back that helps protect it.

   烏龜的背上有堅硬的殼來保護自己。

Answer

1. swim	2. sneaking	3. sun
4. took	5. tree	6. turtle

Uu

ugly 醜陋的；難看的 adj. [ˋʌglɪ]

A blobfish sure is ugly. In fact, it was voted the ugliest animal in the world. They can be found in the ocean around Australia.

水滴魚真的很難看。事實上，牠被選為世界上最醜的動物。可以在澳洲附近的海域找到牠們。

umbrella 雨傘 n. [ʌmˋbrɛlə]

An umbrella that is made to protect someone from the sun is called a parasol. But, of course, most umbrellas are made to protect someone from rain.

一把用來保護人不受太陽照射的雨傘稱做陽傘。但是，當然的，大多數雨傘都是避免讓人被雨淋濕。

under 在……下面 prep. [ˋʌndɚ]

You can find a bunch of
creatures under a rock.
Worms, ants, spiders, beetles
all like to live under rocks.

你可以在岩石下找到一堆生
物。蠕蟲、螞蟻、蜘蛛、甲蟲
都喜歡生活在岩石下。

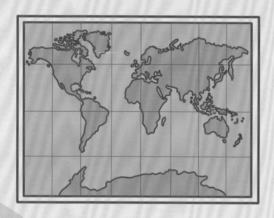

underwater 在水下；
在海面下 adv. [ˋʌndɚˏwɔtɚ]

Most of the planet is
underwater. Less than 29%
of the world is above water.

地球上大部分的地區都在水
面以下。世界上不到百分之
二十九的地區在水面以上。

unicorn 獨角獸 n. [ˋjunɪˏkɔrn]

The unicorn is an imaginary
animal that looks like a horse
with a horn in the middle of its
forehead. They are usually white
and very strong. Some can even
fly.

獨角獸看起來像是額頭中間有一個
角的馬,是一種虛構的動物。牠們
通常是白色的且非常結實。有些甚至能飛。

unique 獨特的；與眾不同的 adj. [ju`nik]

Hippos are quite unique because
their milk is pink! I wonder if it
tastes like strawberry milk?

河馬相當地獨特，因為牠們的奶
是粉紅色的！我在想它的味道是
否像草莓牛奶？

until 直到……時 prep. [ən`tɪl]

Trains were invented before cars. Trains
were invented in 1802. Cars weren't
invented until 1885.

火車是在汽車之前發明的。火車是1802年
發明的。汽車直到1885年才發明。

upside down 上下顛倒地；翻轉 adv.

Bats sleep upside down because it is
the perfect way for them to fly away if
something is trying to get them while they
sleep. Unlike birds, bats can't just jump off
the ground and fly. They need to fall first.
As they fall they can open their arms and
catch wind. If a bat falls to the ground, they
have to climb to a high spot and then fall
off into flight.

蝙蝠顛倒著睡覺，因為如
果有什麼東西試圖在他們
睡覺時抓住牠們，這是牠
們飛走得最佳方式。與鳥
類不同，蝙蝠不能從地面
跳起來就飛。牠們必須先
倒回來，同時才可以張開
手臂乘風飛起。如果蝙蝠
跌在地上，牠們必須爬上
高處，墜入空中飛行。

upstairs 在（往）樓上地 adv. [ˋʌpˋstɛrz]

Have you ever gone upstairs and noticed
that it is warmer upstairs than downstairs?
Bats like to live in in attics (the highest part
of a house, right under a house's roof)
because attics are usually dark and warm.
Why are attics usually warmer than the rest
of a house? Hot air rises. Usually higher
floors are warmer. Even in one room, the
ceiling will be warmer than the floor.

你有沒有上樓發現樓上比樓
下溫暖？蝙蝠喜歡住在閣樓
（房子最高的地方，屋頂的
正下方），因為閣樓通常又
暗又溫暖。為什麼閣樓通常
比房子的其他地方溫暖？因
為熱空氣上升。通常較高的
樓層較溫暖。甚至是在房間
裡，天花板也比地板溫暖。

use 使用；利用 v. [juz]

An encyclopedia is a set of books that have a lot of information on many different subjects. Nowadays, if you want to find something out you can use the internet to find more information on a subject. But, you can't always believe what people write on the internet. It is still better to learn about things from books and newspapers. Not all websites check their facts, but books and newspapers usually do.

百科全書是一套關於許多不同的主題的書籍。現今，如果你想找一些東西，你可以用網路找到更多關於某個主題的資訊。但是，你不能總是相信人們在網路上寫的東西。最好還是從書本和報紙上瞭解一些事情。不是所有的網站都核查事實，但書籍和報紙通常會這樣做。

Vv

valley 山谷；溪谷 n. [`vælɪ]

A valley is the land that is between two mountains or hills. Valleys are either made by a river running through them or because two of earth's plates (a huge rock that is part of the ground) never touched.

山谷是介於兩座山或兩個山丘之間的土地。山谷不是由流經的河流所形成，就是因為地球的兩個板塊（巨大的岩石，屬於地面的一部分）從未碰觸過。

vegetable 蔬菜 n. [`vɛdʒətəbḷ]

Do you like to eat vegetables? Even if you don't, you should really try to eat some every day. They have many minerals and vitamins that will make you strong and smart. Plus, eating more vegetables and less meat is good for the planet!

你喜歡吃蔬菜嗎？即使不喜歡，你也應該試著每天吃一些。蔬菜含有豐富的礦物質與維生素會讓你變強壯又聰明。另外，多吃蔬菜少吃肉對地球有好處！

view 觀看；風景 v. / n. [vju]

Do you remember what the tallest mountain the world is called? The tallest mountain is called Mount Everest. The view from the top of Mount Everest is beautiful. You can see other white mountains and the big, beautiful sky.

你記得世界上最高的山叫什麼嗎？最高的山叫珠穆朗瑪峰。珠穆朗瑪峰山頂上的風景很漂亮。你可以看到其他的白色山脈和廣大美麗的天空。

village 村莊；村子 n. [ˈvɪlɪdʒ]

How is a village different from a town or a city? A village is much smaller, and the houses are usually close together.

村莊與城鎮或城市有什麼不同？村莊相較小很多，而且房子之間通常很靠近。

vine 藤蔓 n. [vaɪn]

A vine is a plant that climbs walls and trees. How does it do this? The plant has a stem that grabs onto things like trees as they slowly grow. Why does it do this? A vine tries to get closer to light so it climbs trees to get closer to the sun.

藤蔓是攀爬在牆上和樹上的一種植物。它是如何做到的？藤蔓在慢慢生長時，它的莖會攀附在東西上，像是樹。為什麼會這樣呢？藤蔓會設法接近光線，所以才會攀著樹去靠近太陽。

violin 小提琴 n. [ˌvaɪəˋlɪn]

A violin is a musical instrument with four strings and is played by drawing a bow back and forth across the strings. Can you guess what instrument family it is a part of? Do you think it is from the keyboard family, guitar family, brass family, woodwind family, percussion family, or bowed string family?

小提琴是一種有四根弦的樂器，利用在弦上來回拉弓來演奏。你能猜出它是哪種類別的樂器嗎？你覺得是鍵盤樂器、吉他類、銅管樂器、木管樂器、打擊樂器還是弦樂器呢？

visit 參觀；拜訪 v. [ˋvɪzɪt]

Ask your parents if you can visit the zoo. It's a great place to learn all about nature and wild animals.

問問你的父母你可不可以去參觀動物園。這是一個瞭解大自然和野生動物的好地方。

visitor 遊客 n. [ˋvɪzɪtə]

The Singapore Zoo in Singapore gets 1.7 million visitors every year. Visitors are able to see over 2,800 animals.

新加坡動物園每年有一百七十萬的遊客。遊客可以看到超過兩千八百隻動物。

voice 聲音 n. [vɔɪs]

If you scream or yell too much, you may lose your voice. Why? If you use any part of your body too much, it will get tired or hurt. Your voice is no different. If you keep pushing air through your throat, it will bother your throat and make your voice sound weird. So, instead of yelling, try laughing. Laughing is always much better for you!

如果你一直尖叫或大叫，你可能會失聲。為什麼？如果你過度使用身體的任何部位，都會感到疲倦或受傷。你的聲音也是一樣。如果你不停地擠壓空氣通過你的喉嚨，會讓你的喉嚨不舒服，讓你的聲音聽起來很奇怪。所以，與其大喊大叫，不如試著笑。笑對你總是比較好！

Ahhhhh!!!

volume 音量 n. [ˋvɑljəm]

Just like your voice, you must also protect your ears. If your music is too loud, it will hurt your ears because your ears are working too hard. When you get older, you won't be able to hear as well. So, turn down the volume!

就像你的聲音一樣，你也必須保護你的耳朵。如果你的音樂太大聲，超出你耳朵的負荷量就會受傷。當你年紀漸長，聽力會下降。所以，把音量調小！

vulture 禿鷹；兀鷹 n. [ˋvʌltʃɚ]

Vultures are huge birds that eat other animals that have already died. They are kind of like garbage men, picking up nature's trash.

禿鷹是一種巨大的鳥類，牠們吃其他已經死亡的動物。牠們有點像清潔工，撿大自然的垃圾。

TRY IT

1. Besides bats, sloths also live and sleep _____ for most of their lives.

   除了蝙蝠以外，樹懶一生中大部分的時間也是顛倒著生活和睡覺。

2. I want to go scuba diving so that I can see all the creatures that live _____.

   我想去潛水，這樣就可以看到所有生活在水底下的生物。

3. The young girl knew that the _____ at the circus wasn't real. It was just a white horse with a horn taped to its head.

   小女孩知道馬戲團的獨角獸不是真的。那只是一匹頭上綁著一隻角的白馬。

4. Eat all your _____! Finish your carrots.

   吃掉所有的蔬菜！把你的胡蘿蔔吃完。

5. A _____ is a bowed string musical instrument.

   小提琴是一種弓弦樂器。

6. I would like to go _____ the library today.

   我今天想去參觀圖書館。

Answer

1. upside down   2. underwater   3. unicorn

4. vegetable   5. violin   6. visit

Ww

wait 等待，等候；期盼，盼望 v. [wet]

It takes about one year for a human baby to learn how to walk. Many baby animals, like giraffes and elephants, have to learn to walk as soon as they are born. Why? If their family wants to move somewhere, they won't wait for the babies who can't walk. If the baby animal doesn't know how to walk, it will be left all by itself.

嬰兒需要大約一年的時間學習走路。許多動物寶寶，像是長頸鹿和大象，一出生就必須學會走路。為什麼？如果牠們的家族想要移動到其他地方，牠們不會等待無法走路的寶寶。如果動物寶寶不知道如何走路，牠們將會被獨自留下。

wake 醒來；叫醒，吵醒 v. [wek]

At night, you might hear a quiet chirping sound. That chirping sound might be a cricket. But why do we only hear them at night? Crickets wake up at night. Do you remember what an animal that is awake at night is called?

在晚上，你可能會聽到唧唧叫的聲音。唧唧的叫聲可能來自蟋蟀。但為什麼我們只能在晚上聽見這個聲音？蟋蟀在夜晚活動。你還記得在晚上活動的動物被稱為什麼嗎？

walk 走，步行，行走 v. [wɔk]

A baby learns to stand before it learns to walk, and it learns to crawl before it stands. Can you guess what it learns to do before it learns to crawl?

嬰兒學會走路之前先學會站立，會站立之前先學會爬行。你能猜到在學會爬行之前先學會什麼嗎？

119

walrus 海象 n. [ˈwɔlrəs]

A walrus is a sea creature with two long tusks coming out of its mouth. A tusk is like a very long and sharp tooth. The walrus will use its tusks to pull itself out of the water and onto land. It also shows how old the walrus is and how important it is in its family. The walrus with the biggest tusk is the most important in the family.

海象是一種嘴巴有兩支長長牙的海洋生物。長牙是非常長且尖銳的牙齒。長象會用牠的長牙把自己從水里拉上岸。它也顯示海象的年紀有多大及在家族裡的地位有多重要。有最大長牙的海象在家族裡的地位是最高的。

warm 溫暖的；暖和的 adj. [wɔrm]

If you want to stay warm, put a hat on! Much of your body's heat comes out of the head.

如果你想要保持溫暖，戴上帽子！你身體大部份的熱能都來自於頭部。

wash 洗，清洗，洗滌 v. [wɑʃ]

Is your mom or dad always telling you to wash your hands? It is important to wash your hands before you eat or touch your face. Germs are everywhere and when they get into your body, germs can make you very sick.

你的爸爸媽媽是否常常告訴你要洗手？在你吃東西或碰觸你的臉之前洗手是很重要的。細菌充斥著各個角落，當細菌進入你的身體時會令你生病。

water 水 n. [`wɔtɚ]

Your brain and body are made up of a lot of water. Actually, most of your brain and body is water. This makes it even more important to always drink water. The more water you drink, the more balanced you will feel. Your body needs water!

你的大腦和身體由大量的水組成。事實上，你的大腦和身體大部份都是水。這使得多喝水變得更重要。你喝的水越多，你會感覺越平衡。你的身體需要水份！

wave （尤指海上的）浪，波浪，波濤 n. [wev]

A wave's size depends on things like wind speed, how long wind blows for, and where the wind is blowing from. Sometimes waves can be blown in a certain way that causes a rip current. Rip currents are very dangerous because they arc waves that will pull you out away from the beach and further into the sea.

波浪的大小取決於風速、風吹的時間有多長以及風從哪裡吹來。有時候風從特定的方向吹來會導致離岸流。離岸流是非常危險的，因為它會把你帶離海邊甚至捲入海中。

wave 揮舞，揮動；擺動，搖晃 v. [wev]

It is hard to swim out of a rip current, so if you are caught in a rip current, you should wave for help to someone on shore (on the beach).

要游離開離岸流是非常困難的，所以當你被捲入離岸流時，你應該向岸上（在海灘上）的人揮手求救。

wear 穿（衣服）；戴（首飾等） v. [wɛr]

Why don't dogs need to wear shoes? Doesn't that hurt their feet? If it is very hot outside, it is not good to let your dog walk on roads or sidewalks. The sun can make the ground very hot, and that will burn their feet. If it is very hot, try not to walk your dog on roads and sidewalks.

為什麼狗不需要穿鞋子？這樣牠們的腳不會受傷嗎？如果外面很熱的話，最好不要讓你的狗走在馬路上或人行道上。太陽會讓地面變得很燙，並燙傷牠們的腳。如果很熱的話，別在馬路上或人行道上遛狗。

weather 天氣；氣象 n. [ˋwɛðɚ]

Dogs have tough paws that make it okay to walk on things like grass and stones even in very hot weather.

狗有堅硬的爪子讓牠們即使在很熱的天氣還是可以在草地或是石頭上行走。

whale 鯨 n. [hwel]

Whales are the largest animals on earth. Some whales can be almost as big as a basketball court!

鯨魚是世界上最大的動物。有些鯨魚幾乎可以跟籃球場一樣大！

wheel 輪子；車輪 n. [hwil]

Before wheels were used on carts and cars, they were actually used by artists to make pots and bowls!

在輪子被用在馬車及車子前，它們實際上是被藝術家用來製作鍋碗瓢盆！

whisker （貓、鼠等動物的）鬍鬚
n. [`hwɪskə]

What do you think animals use their whiskers for? Whiskers are a good way for animals to feel things that it may not see. This is very useful when an animal needs to walk around in the dark.

你認為動物用牠們的鬍鬚做什麼？鬍鬚是動物用來感覺牠們看不到的東西時的好方法。當動物需要在黑暗中行走時這是個很好用的方法。

white 白色的；雪白的；乳白的 adj. [hwaɪt]

If you put a white piece of paper next to a black piece of paper outside in the sun for a few minutes, the black piece of paper will feel warmer than the white paper. Why? Black absorbs light and white reflects light. So, the black paper will take in more heat and the white will push the heat away.

如果你在陽光下把一張白色和一張黑色的紙放個幾分鐘，黑色的紙感覺會比白色的更加溫暖。為什麼？黑色吸收光而白色反射光。所以黑色的紙接收到更多熱能而白色的紙則推開熱能。

windy 颱風的；多風的 adj.
[`wɪndɪ]

Do you think waves are bigger or smaller on a windy day?

你覺得在颱風的日子裡海浪會變大還是變小？

wonder 疑惑；想知道 v. [`wʌndɚ]

Have you ever wondered what it would be like to be a fish living in the ocean?

你有沒有想像過當一隻魚生活在海裡會是什麼樣子？

wool 羊毛；動物毛 n. [wul]

Wool is so warm that humans use it to make sweaters, hats, gloves, and scarves. Sheep also need their wool. It's the only way they can keep warm in the winter.

羊毛很溫暖，所以人們拿來做成毛衣、帽子、手套和圍巾。綿羊同樣需要羊毛。這是牠們在冬天唯一的保暖方式。

world 地球，世界 n. [wɜld]

There are 195 countries in the world. When you grow up, how many countries do you think you will visit?

世界上有一百九十五個國家。你覺得當你長大後你能去拜訪幾個國家？

127

Xx

x-ray X光 n. [ˋɛksˏre]

X-rays let out radiation. Radiation is good because it can go through things that something like light cannot. This lets us see what is inside of a body or a suitcase. Radiation is bad, though, because too much of it can make you very sick.

X射線釋放出輻射。輻射的好處是它可以穿透東西,而像光則不行。這可以讓我們看到身體或是行李箱裡有什麼。然而輻射也有壞處,過多的輻射可能會讓你生病。

xylophone 木琴 n. [ˋzaɪləˏfon]

A xylophone is a musical instrument that is part of the percussion family. Other instruments that are part of the percussion family are drums and bells. Other musical instrument families are keyboard, guitar, brass, woodwind, and bowed string.

木琴是打擊樂器家族的一份子。其他同是打擊樂器家族的還有鼓和鈴。其他樂器家族有鍵盤、吉他、銅管、貝斯、木管樂器及弓弦樂器。

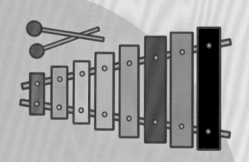

TRY IT

1. Crickets are nocturnal animals that _____ up at night and go to sleep in the day.
   蟋蟀是在夜晚活動而白天睡覺的夜行性動物。

2. A baby learns to sit, then crawl, then stand, then _____.
   嬰兒學會坐，接著爬，再來站，然後走。

3. You can find _____ in any ocean in the world.
   在世界上的任何海域都可以發現鯨魚的蹤跡。

4. When I broke my leg, the doctor could see my broken bone with an _____.
   當我骨折時，醫生可以用X光看到我骨折的骨頭。

5. This candle is made from bees_____.
   這個蠟燭是用蜜蠟製成的。

6. When I _____ blue and red, I get purple.
   當我混合藍色和紅色，我會得到紫色。

Answer
1. wake
2. walk
3. whales
4. x-ray
5. wax
6. mix

yacht 帆船；快艇；遊艇 n. [jɑt]

There are many different types of
boats. (What kinds can you name?
Sailboats, row boat, fishing boat,
ship……anything else?) There is
also a boat called a yacht. It is used
for people who want to sail out to sea
and stay out at sea overnight.

有許多不同類型的船。（你能說出幾
種？帆船、划艇、漁船、輪船…還有
哪些？）還有一種船叫做遊艇。它被
用於想出海並在海上過夜的人。

Yesterday　　Today

yesterday 昨天 n. [ˋjɛstɚde]

What did you do yesterday?
What will you do today?

你昨天做了什麼？
你今天要做什麼？

yard 院子；天井；
庭院 n. [jɑrd]

Yards are covered in
grass and is a great
place for kids to play,
pretend, and explore.

庭院裡會覆蓋青草而
且是孩子玩耍、假裝
和探索的好地方。

yellow 黃色 n. [ˋjɛlo]

If you mix the colors blue and
yellow together, you make the
color green!

如果你將藍色及黃色混合，
你會得到綠色！

131

yoga 瑜伽 n. [ˋjogə]

Yoga is a type of exercise that helps you stretch your body. Many adults practice yoga, but it's also good for kids. Maybe you should try some yoga!

瑜珈是一種可以幫助你舒展四肢的運動。許多大人會練瑜珈，不過這對小孩子其實也很好。也許你也可以嘗試看看！

you 你；你們 pronoun. [ju]

There is no one else in the world like you. You are very special. What makes you different from your friends? What makes you the same?

在這個世界上你是獨一無二的。
你是最特別的。
是什麼讓你跟朋友間有所不同？
又是什麼讓你們相同？

young 幼小的；年輕的 adj. [jʌŋ]

When you are young, your brain learns things very quickly. The older you get, the harder it becomes. So, open your English book and start learning English!

當你年輕的時候，你的大腦學習事物非常快。當你年紀越大，會變得越困難。所以，打開你的英文課本開始學習英文吧！

yo-yo 溜溜球 n. [ˋjoˌjo]

Have you ever played with a yo-yo? Many years ago, astronauts brought a yo-yo into space. The astronauts wanted to see if they could play with it without gravity. Well, when they pushed the yo-yo down, it worked, but it wouldn't sleep. When a yo-yo sleeps, it gets to the bottom of the string and keeps spinning there before it comes back up. When the astronauts tried, the yo-yo went down but came right back up.

你玩過溜溜球嗎？很多年前，太空人將溜溜球帶到太空。太空人想知道能不能在無重力的情況下玩溜溜球。他們可以成功讓溜溜球下降但無法靜止。當溜溜球靜止，它到達繩子的底端並持續自轉直到收回。當太空人嘗試時，溜溜球下降但又立刻回到手上。

Zz

zany 稀奇古怪的；荒謬可笑的 adj. [ˋzenɪ]

A zorilla isn't a zany gorilla. It's actually a weasel that looks a bit like a skunk. They live in Africa and are known as the African skunk.

非洲艾虎並不是一種滑稽的大猩猩。牠其實是一種看起來像臭鼬的鼬屬。牠們居住在非洲，被稱為非洲臭鼬。

zebra 斑馬 n. [ˋzibrə]

Zebras look a lot like horses with stripes, but they actually are not horses. Zebras are much meaner and more dangerous. They will bite and kick and can even kill a lion.

斑馬看起來很像有條紋的馬，但牠們其實不是馬。斑馬更兇且更危險。牠們會咬人踢人，甚至可以殺死一隻獅子。

zephyr 和風，微風 n. [ˋzɛfɚ]

A gentle zephyr can blow a brown leaf off the tree. Why do you think a zephyr can blow a brown leaf off a tree, but not a green leaf?

輕柔的微風可以吹落樹上的褐色葉子。你覺得為什麼微風可以吹落褐色葉子而不是綠色葉子？

zest （柑桔類水果的）果皮 n. [zɛst]

The zest of a citrus fruit is the outer skin. On an orange, it's that shiny orange part and on a lemon it's the shiny yellow part. Many people use the zest because it has a special flavor.

柑橘類水果的果皮是外層的皮。在橘子上，是橘色有光澤的部分，而在檸檬是黃色有光澤的部分。很多人使用果皮是因為它有特別的風味。

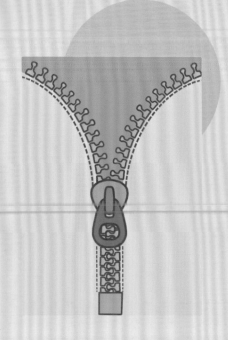

zipper 拉鍊 n. [ˈzɪpɚ]

The zipper used to only be used on boots. People started to used zippers on clothes in the 1930s. Before that, clothes only had buttons.

拉鍊以前只用在靴子上。在1930年代人們開始將拉鍊使用在衣服上。在那之前，衣服只會使用鈕扣。

zoo 動物園 n. [zu]

Many zoos are a fun place to visit and learn about animals. A good zoo will help protect animals, give animals a safe place to live, and do research to help us learn more about them.

動物園是參觀及學習動物的有趣地方。一個好的動物園會保護動物，給動物一個安全的地方居住且做研究幫助我們更加了解牠們。

TRY IT

1. Mixing _____ and red makes the color orange.
   混合黃色和紅色得到橘色。

2. After we shear the wool off of this sheep, we will spin the wool into a long piece of _____.
   將羊毛從羊身上剪下來後，我們會將羊毛紡成很長的紗線。

3. Someone who is very good at _____ is called a yogi. A yogi can teach you how to do this type of exercise.
   很會瑜珈的人稱為瑜珈老師。瑜珈老師可以教你怎麼做這項運動。

4. If I have three apples, and I give you all three apples, then I have _____ apples left.
   如果我有三顆蘋果，而我將所有的蘋果都給你，那我就沒有剩下蘋果了。

5. The car _____ past my house. It was so fast!
   汽車從我家駛過。車速好快！

6. I want to go to the _____ to see the zebras and giraffes.
   我想去動物園看斑馬和長頸鹿。

Answer
1. yellow	2. yarn	3. yoga
4. zero	5. zoomed	6. zoo

Vocabulary

蘋果 apple [ˋæpḷ]

草莓 strawberry [ˋstrɔbɛrɪ]

葡萄 grape [grep]

奇異果 kiwi [ˋkiwɪ]

香蕉 banana [bəˋnænə]

橘子 orange [ˋɔrɪndʒ]

蕃茄 tomato [tə`meto]

櫻桃 cherry [`tʃɛrɪ]

木瓜 papaya [pə`paɪə]

酪梨 avocado [ˌævə`kɑdo]

西瓜 watermelon [`wɔtɚˌmɛlən]

鳳梨 pineapple [`paɪnˌæpl̩]

Vocabulary

熊 bear [bɛr]

長頸鹿 giraffe [dʒə`ræf]

河馬 hippo [`hɪpo]

獅子 lion [`laɪən]

松鼠 squirrel [`skwɝəl]

兔子 rabbit [`ræbɪt]

準備好迎接大富翁闖關遊戲囉！

大富翁闖關規則：請先將人物卡剪下，選擇自己喜愛的角色，當闖關者遇到有標註中文的圖片時請將此單字正確的拼出，若是遇到填空問題時請正確的說出此單字，答對問題時將可以前進一格若答錯將停留在原地。

蛇 snake [snek]

水豚 capybara [kæpəˋbarə]

無尾熊 koala [koˋɑlə]

貓熊 panda [ˋpændə]

猴子 monkey [ˋɛləfənt]

烏龜 turtle [ˋtɝtl̩]

動物大富翁

水果大富翁

探險大富翁

大富翁解答

動物大富翁

1. muscles
2. Squirrels
3. bat
4. giraffe
5. animals
6. bee
7. butterfly
8. elephant
9. sloth
10. Crabs

水果大富翁

1. vegetables
2. farm
3. healthy
4. mushrooms
5. onion
6. orange
7. pumpkin
8. grapes
9. tea
10. strawberries

探險大富翁

1. colors
2. ocean
3. dig
4. east
5. gas
6. nature
7. recycle
8. dolphins
9. land
10. mountain

國家圖書館出版品預行編目(CIP)資料

用英文說故事，多的是你不知道的事 / Jennifer
　Lee作；Sunny Chang譯. -- 初版. -- 新北
　市；銀河文化，2020. 04
　　　面；　公分
　ISBN 978-986-98652-1-0 (精裝)

1.英語 2.讀本

805.18　　　　　　　　　　　109001896

用英文說故事，多的是你不知道的事
I Wonder Why for Kid

作　　　者　Jennifer Lee

譯　　　者　Sunny Chang

主　　　編　徐梓軒

責任編輯　張昀、劉沛萱

校　　　對　秦怡如、Anson Liu

插　　　畫　米蟲女孩

行銷企劃　梁蔓容

封面設計　江孟達

內文排版　李雅玲

出　　　版　銀河文化

地　　　址　236新北市土城區忠承路89號6樓

初版一刷　2020年04月

定　　　價　新台幣380元 / 港幣127元

總 經 銷　創智文化有限公司

　　　　　地址：236新北市土城區忠承路89號6樓

　　　　　電話：886-2-2268-3489

　　　　　傳真：886-2-2269-6560

人物卡

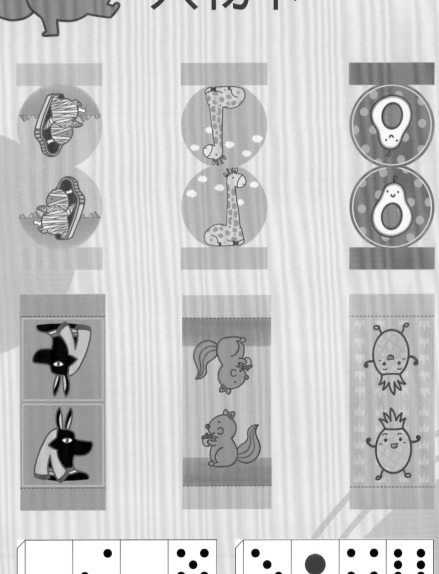

貼心小提醒：請直接剪下摺起即可，不需使用膠水黏貼。